TIGER MOTH

THE PEST SHOW ON EARTH

Librarian Reviewer
Katharine Kan

Reading Consultant
Elizabeth Stedem

www.raintreepublishers.co.uk
Visit our website to find out
more information about
Raintree books.

To order:
☎ Phone 0845 6044371
📄 Fax +44 (0) 1865 312263
✉ Email myorders@raintreepublishers.co.uk

Customers from outside the UK please telephone +44 1865 312262

Raintree is an imprint of Capstone Global Library Limited, a company incorporated
in England and Wales having its registered office at 7 Pilgrim Street, London,
EC4V 6LB – Registered company number: 6695582

Text © Stone Arch Books 2008
First published in hardback and paperback in the United Kingdom
by Capstone Global Library in 2010
The moral rights of the proprietor have been asserted.

Art Director: Heather Kindseth
Designer: Brann Garvey
Editor: Vaarunika Dharmapala
Originated by Capstone Global Library Ltd
Printed and bound in China by Leo Paper Products Ltd

ISBN 978 1 406216 59 2 (hardback)
14 13 12 11 10
10 9 8 7 6 5 4 3 2 1

ISBN 978 1 406216 68 4 (paperback)
14 13 12 11 10
10 9 8 7 6 5 4 3 2 1

British Library Cataloguing in Publication Data
A full catalogue record for this book is available from the British Library.

TIGER MOTH

THE PeST SHOW ON EARTH

by Aaron Reynolds   illustrated by Erik Lervold

CAST OF CHARACTERS

Mrs Mandible

Tiger Moth

Kung Pow

She was wrong about that. Because suddenly . . .

Gather one and all!

Experience the "Pest Show on Earth"!

It looks like the carnival is in town, children.

What were the chances?

I suppose the times tables can wait. It's almost three, after all.

Class dismissed!

Yay!

Those carnival bugs may not have all their antennae, but they have great timing.

I was caught up in the fun and had let my ninja guard down.

Wait a minute, Kung.

Do you see what I see?

Yeah! Clover candyfloss!

No. Look at what's in the ringmaster's hand!

I know that cane!

That's no cane.

It's a sword in disguise!

Remember, you almost got shish-kebabbed by it once.

That means the ringmaster is . . .

Later that night, the town swarmed to the carnival for the food and games.

But Kung Pow and I had work to do.

Thanks to our ninja skills, we blended into the shadows of the main tent.

We were almost invisible.

Ouch! I stubbed my toe.

Almost . . .

Listen, I know that voice.

Weevil!

12

14

21

About the author

Aaron Reynolds loves insects and loves books, so Tiger Moth was a perfect blend of both. Reynolds is the author of several great books for children, including *Chicks and Salsa,* which *Publishers Weekly* called "a literary fandango". Reynolds had no idea what "fandango" meant. After looking it up in the dictionary, he learned the word means "playful and silly behaviour." Reynolds hopes to write several more fandangos in the future. He lives with his wife, two children, and four insect-obsessed cats.

About the illustrator

Erik Lervold was born in Puerto Rico, a small island in the Caribbean, and has been a professional painter. Deciding that he wanted to be a full-time artist, he attended the Minneapolis College of Art and Design, studied Comic Art, and graduated in 2004. Erik teaches classes in libraries and has taught art in the Minnesota Children's Museum. He loves the colour green and has a collection of really big goggles. He also loves sandwiches. If you want him to be your friend, bring him a roast beef sandwich and he will love you forever.

Glossary

apprentice young person that learns a skill from a more experienced person. This definition applies to insects as well.

buffet meal where guests serve themselves from many choices of foods laid out on a table

disguise something worn to hide a person or object's true identity; a mask is a type of disguise

exoskeleton bony shell covering the outside of some insects

finale last part of a show

mothball something used to keep pesky moths away from clothing

ringmaster person in charge of a circus. Weevil pretended to be a ringmaster, but really he's just an evil bug.

secured completely locked up with no chance of escape

shish-kebabbed be treated like a shish kebab, or a piece of meat or vegetable cooked on a skewer

soul another word for person, or in this case, insect

villain an evil person . . . or evil insect

More about travelling shows

People have enjoyed travelling carnivals, circuses, and other festivals for centuries. During the Middle Ages, about 1,000 to 1,500 years ago, European villagers were entertained by performers called minstrels, who sang songs, put on plays, or told stories.

During the 1500s, laws stopped minstrels from travelling from town to town. But these laws didn't stop the shows. Instead, performers set up permanent buildings for their acts in towns across Europe.

In the early 1800s, many people lived too far away to travel to town for entertainment. In 1825, J. Purdy Brown had an idea to make the circus building out of canvas instead of wood. The canvas tent could be carried and set up closer to the customers.

Many early circuses moved their equipment with horses and wagons. These shows could only travel about 30 kilometres (18 miles) a day. In 1872, Phineas Taylor Barnum started one of the first circuses to travel by train. They could reach more cities and more people.

In 1881, P. T. Barnum and James Anthony Bailey joined together and created the Barnum & Bailey circus. They called their circus "The Greatest Show on Earth."

In 1893, one of today's most popular carnival rides was created, the first Ferris Wheel. Invented by George W. Ferris, the ride stood 264 feet tall and could carry 2,160 passengers at a time.

Travelling carnivals combined the acts found at a circus with the rides found at a fair. Carnivals also had a display of weird and strange objects or people. This display was known as the sideshow. Early sideshows included fire-eaters, two-headed cows, and sword swallowers.

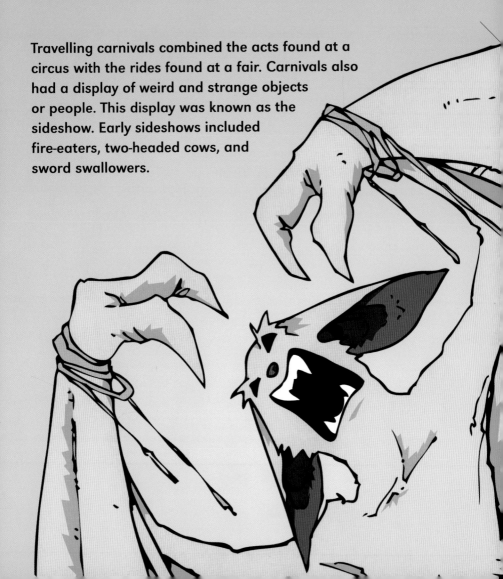

Discussion questions

1. How does Kung Pow help out Tiger Moth in this story? Do you think Tiger could have defeated Weevil without his young apprentice? Explain your answer using examples from the story.

2. At the end of the story, Weevil is carried off by Wing Kong. Do you think this is the last time Tiger and Kung will have to face him? Why or why not?

3. This book was written and illustrated by two different people. If you had a choice, would you rather be an author or an illustrator? Explain your decision.

Writing prompts

1. Except for the deadly Wing Kong, all of the characters in this story are insects. Choose your favourite insect, and write your own story about it.

2. Where a story takes place is called the setting. The setting of this story is a carnival. Write a completely different adventure for Tiger Moth or Kung Pow using the same setting.

3. Have you ever been to a carnival, fair, or an amusement park? Describe your experience. What were your favourite rides, games, and foods?

More amazing adventures!

When Zack Allen is bullied at school, he invents a robot super suit to help him fight evil in the playground and beyond. He becomes Zinc Alloy, the world's newest superhero!